Essential WORD SORTS

By Laura Woodard and Amy Coit

Really Good Stuff Publishing

Fun & creative teaching resources for today's classroom™

Acknowledgments

We thank Ken Poe for his helpful guidance, teachers Kelly Daher and Tonja Worthley for their informed feedback, and our friends and families for their support. Thanks also to the 1st and 2nd grade students at Calabasas Elementary School in Watsonville, California, who helped us test these word sorts and activities.

For information regarding permission, write to:
Really Good Stuff,
448 Pepper St,
Monroe, CT 06468.
1-800-366-1920
www.reallygoodstuff.com

Printed in Canada

10 9 8 7 6 5 4 3 2

ISBN 1-888142-71-5

Contents

Introduction

Word Sorting Now!

Word sorting is an essential, hands-on way to teach reading and spelling. When students examine words and compare them by word features in a sequence that promotes language learning, they improve their spelling skills, increase reading fluency, and build wider vocabularies.

Using word sorts in repetitive classroom and homework activities, students will begin to recognize spelling patterns automatically, and then put them to use in their reading and writing. Now we've made it easy for you to incorporate a comprehensive word sorting program into your language arts instruction with these ready-to-use sorts and extension activities.

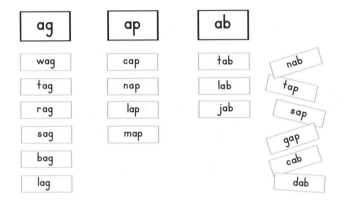

Essential Word Sorts is a complete and customizable set of word sorts that will help your students acquire important language skills at the early stages of literacy. The words in these sorts represent the language that young children encounter most frequently in their reading.

In addition, the word family and short/long vowel sorts include examples of all of the thirty-seven basic phonograms identified by researchers Richard E. Wylie and Donald D. Durrell in 1970. Phonograms, or rimes, and the word families that can be built from them are fundamental building blocks of phonics instruction. Recognizing these common chunks facilitates decoding, which in turn builds fluency.

How To Use Essential Word Sorts

The sorts are organized in a sequence appropriate to the way children learn to read and write. Following a simple, familiar review of beginning sound word sorts,

your students should be ready to complete the simple CVC word family sorts in Section II, and then the beginning blends and digraphs in Section III, and finally the short, long and r-controlled vowel sounds.

Begin a new type of word sort with plenty of modeling before distributing the student sorts. (See Word Sorting Lesson on page 5 for detailed steps.) Copy the needed word sort pages for your students. **Don't cut up the originals!** This book is meant to be copied and used again and again. (See Management and Storage, page 4.)

Section Introductions and Suggested Activities

We lead into each section by describing how the sorts fit into your students' word study and spelling instruction. You get important tips and special notes on teaching the word features in that section. There are also suggestions for extending the sort work through interactive and creative activities such as card games, partner challenges, and personalized sort books. (See Reinforcement, page 6.)

Word Sorts

Each sort has up to five categories that isolate spelling patterns students need to master at the early stages of literacy. There are as many as six sort words for each category, and you are encouraged to add words using the blank cards provided (see Blank Sort Cards, page 145).

The word sorts are in four spelling skill areas (Beginning Consonant Sounds Review, Short Vowel Word Families, etc.) that are further classified by the specific word features being sorted. The word feature categories (CVC words, CVCC words, etc.) are noted at the top of each sort. Some sections include a Review sort.

"Other" Category

Starting with the short vowel sorts in Section IV some of the sorts include an additional category for exceptions, which go in an **other** column. The **other** words included in the sorts defy rules of long and short vowel sounds though they follow the spelling patterns. For example, in the **short a** vs. **short o** sort (Sort # 84), the word **was**, following the CVC rule, would be pronounced with a short **a** sound, but the **a** in **was** is actually pronounced like a short **u**, making the word an exception, or **other**.

Shown here, **was** is not a **short a** word and should go in the **other** category:

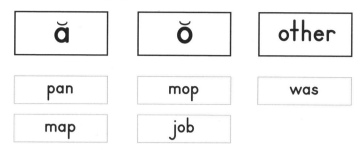

You can add an **other** category using your own words to any sort.

Blank Sort Cards
Use the *Blank Sort Cards Reproducible* on page 145 for making your own word sorts or for adding your own words to the sorts in this book. You can fill in the words before copying the sort, or write words on the board for the students to copy onto blank cards you provide.

After sorting all the words provided, the group can brainstorm other words that fit the categories and add them to the sort. For independent sorts, you can challenge students to think of extra sort words, write them onto blank cards, and place them under the appropriate categories.

Reproducibles
The final section of *Essential Word Sorts*, beginning on page 141, is devoted to reproducible management forms and other materials that make it easier to do the extension activities described in the beginning of each section.

Teaching with Word Sorts

It's important to teach the word sorts at an appropriate pace for students at different reading levels. Students at earlier levels, for example, will need more repeated practice with the sorts before completing them independently.

Although the sorts in *Essential Word Sorts* contain important sight words, many sight words do not follow standard spelling rules, and require lessons devoted to sight word study. Also remember, kids enjoy word sorting, but they will not be fully engaged by sorts alone. We strongly recommend that you have students apply their word sorting skills with fun activities. You can find suggestions for games and other activities in every section's introduction, and in the reproducibles.

In order to ensure students are progressing with their reading and spelling, it is helpful to group your students by instructional level based on your assessments. The homogeneous groupings are effective in planning word sorting activities, as students at different levels work at varying paces and benefit from different amounts of support and practice.

Sorting by Word Features
In word sorting, students look at word features that occur in their reading. Therefore, you should select sorts that match their reading abilities and that will challenge them.

On the following page is a general timeline to show how the spelling stages coincide with the spelling patterns studied in the word sorts.

Beginning Consonant Sounds
This is a brief review of beginning sound sorting that students have already done at the emergent level.

Short Vowel Word Families
Students sort familiar three- and four-letter rhyming words into word families.

Blends and Digraphs
Students distinguish easy consonant combinations that begin or end familiar words.

Short, Long, and R-Controlled Vowels
Students listen for long and short vowel sounds, compare common long vowel patterns, and differentiate r-controlled vowels.

For more information about sorting by these word features, see the introduction for each section.

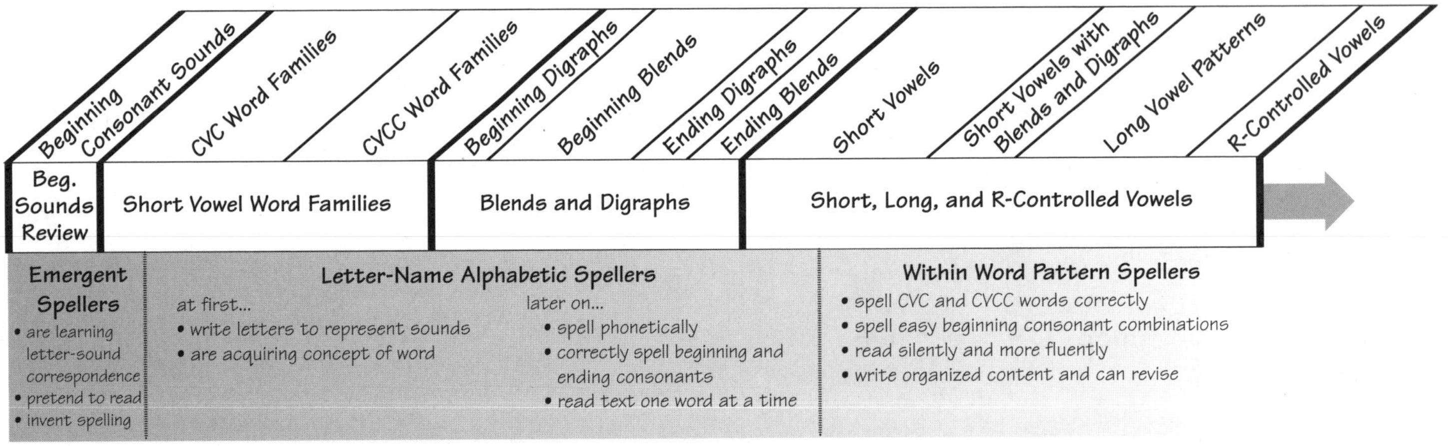

The top diagonal labels (left to right):
Beginning Consonant Sounds | CVC Word Families | CVCC Word Families | Beginning Digraphs | Beginning Blends | Ending Digraphs | Ending Blends | Short Vowels | Short Vowels with Blends and Digraphs | Long Vowel Patterns | R-Controlled Vowels

| Beg. Sounds Review | Short Vowel Word Families | Blends and Digraphs | Short, Long, and R-Controlled Vowels | → |

Emergent Spellers	Letter-Name Alphabetic Spellers		Within Word Pattern Spellers
• are learning letter-sound correspondence • pretend to read • invent spelling	at first... • write letters to represent sounds • are acquiring concept of word	later on... • spell phonetically • correctly spell beginning and ending consonants • read text one word at a time	• spell CVC and CVCC words correctly • spell easy beginning consonant combinations • read silently and more fluently • write organized content and can revise

Ways to Administer Word Sorts:

- **Teacher demonstration** – teacher demonstrates for small group
- **Independent sorts** – students sort word cards on their own at their desks or in literacy centers
- **Partner sorts** – students pair up for word sorting activities (Activity Card on page 149)
- **Homework sorts** – students take home the reproducible word sorts
- **One-on-One sorts** – teacher guides student sorts

Types of Sorts:

- **Closed sort (most word sorting)** – teacher directs the sort by giving the categories
- **Open sort** – students see patterns and sort words into categories they determine (Activity Card Reproducible on page 148)
- **Blind sort** – students hear a sort word and point to the appropriate category card (Activity Card Reproducible on page 150)
- **Picture/word sort** – category and/or sort cards include picture cues for added support
- **Written sort** – students write sorted words onto a blank grid (Blank Sorting Grid Reproducible on page 145)
- **Speed sort** – students complete timed sorts to gain automatic recognition of word features (Activity Card Reproducible on page 147)
- **Word hunt** – students search their reading materials for words that fit designated categories
- **Sorting with tiles** – students sort with plastic or magnetic word tiles for kinesthetic reinforcement

Literacy Centers

The reproducible word sorts lend themselves well to student literacy centers. Groups or individuals visit an area of the room designated for language skills reinforcement activities. You can provide laminated word sorts or other word sorting challenges for students to complete before moving to the next station. Students may visit stations alone or in partners. Working in pairs they can take turns checking each other's work, doing timed sorts (switching off as time keepers, students try to beat their own time), or completing a variety of other partner tasks.

Home Connection

Before you begin word sorting, send a note home to parents and guardians letting them know what word sorting is and why it's important (see *Parent/Guardian Letter Reproducible* on pages 141 and 142). When students have had plenty of word sorting practice in the classroom, you can start copying and sending home the word sorts as homework assignments. You can also make copies of the Activity Card Reproducibles (pages 147 to 150) for family members' reference.

Management and Storage

Make sure only to cut up copies of the sorts, not the originals. You will find it is easier to manage this book of sorts when you keep the original intact.

Look over the word sorts, select sorts you expect to demonstrate for each group in the coming week, and make copies of those pages for the students. Have the students cut up their own sort cards as part of the assignment. It is helpful, before cutting up the sorts to laminate the ones you intend to use repeatedly in literacy centers. You can also use the durable laminated cards for one-on-one demonstrations and support.

Helpful storage materials for student and demonstration-size word sort cards are available through Really Good Stuff®. These include word sort Storage Pages in two sizes and storage containers for card materials, magnetic sorts, and more.

Support Materials

Demonstration-size word sort cards, student sorting activity books, student sorting mats, games, and other items can be made or purchased to use in conjunction with the sorts in this book. Additional materials can add versatility, variety, and fun to your class' word sorting. (See Reinforcement, page 6.)

Evaluation

After students complete the sorts and activities related to a particular word feature, evaluate their learning in a way that authentically reflects their word knowledge. For example, in their weekly spelling tests, instead of just asking your students to spell every word from a spelling list, which merely tests their memorization skills, include a sample of sort words and some other words that have the same orthographic pattern. This way you are asking them to apply their word knowledge, and their performance will guide your instruction for the next week. You may discover that one group needs to revisit some word features while another group is ready to move on. The *Word Sort Record Sheet Reproducible* can assist in this evaluation process.

Record Sheet

Keep track of the completed sorts and your evaluations for each group or individual. The *Word Sort Record Sheet Reproducible* included on pages 143 and 144 makes this easy. Fill in the numbered boxes to show the completion status of each sort. One option is to use a simple color coding system to reflect levels of completion for each sort. For example, you could use a lighter colored marking, such as yellow, to indicate a sort you have done once that needs further attention. A red dot could mean the sort was very challenging for the student or group. A box completely filled with a darker color such as blue could indicate you have revisited the sort on a different day and students show understanding of the word features. Or you can simply X out completed sorts. There is plenty of space to write comments or list problem words.

The *Word Sort Record Sheet Reproducible* can serve as both an agenda and an assessment record of spelling work, and is helpful in communications with parents.

Word Sorting Lesson

Small Group Demonstration

Lead a small group demonstration whenever you introduce a new type of sort, focus on a different word feature, or notice that students need additional modeling. For optimum visibility, sets of demonstration cards for *Essential Word Sorts* and a 4-Column Word Sorting Desktop Pocket Chart are available for purchase through Really Good Stuff®. Here is one of many possible ways to model a closed word sort:

1. Select two or more categories for a word feature (for example **ap, ip,** and **op**) and set up a pocket chart in a visible position.
2. Hold up each word card and read the word with the group, offering support as necessary.
3. Select one word card and say the word, such as **nap**. Ask the group if **nap** sounds like **ap, ip,** or **op**. When the correct category is named, place the category card at the top of the pocket chart.
4. Using the method described in step 3, display all three category cards.
5. As you continue, sort words by comparing them to the other words in each category: "Does **hip** sound like **nap, zip,** or **mop**?"
6. Sort all of the word cards this way.
7. Repeat the demonstration, this time asking students to sort the word cards in the pocket chart after you've introduced the categories.
8. Reflect on the sort with your group. Talk about how the words are alike and different, and what challenges the students had.

ap	ip	op
nap	zip	mop
cap	dip	hop
sap	hip	
	tip	

top
map

Independent Sorting

After modeling the word sort for the group, have students do the sort independently:

1. Make a copy of the sort for each student.
2. Make sure students first read all the words and set aside words they have trouble reading so they can revisit them for further practice.

3. Have students cut out all the cards and place the category cards in a row along the top of their desk or sorting surface.

ap	ip	op
nap	hip	hop
tip	zip	map
mop	top	lop
sap	gap	sip
dip	pop	cap
tap	rip	sop

4. Have students sort the cards by reading each word aloud and placing it under the appropriate category.

5. Have students check their own sorts by reading all the words in each category aloud.

6. Check the sorts or have student partners check each other's sorts. If students have made errors, tell them how many and give them time to find and correct the mistakes.

Reinforcement

Word sorting is most effective and engaging when you combine it with fun and varied word work activities. This is especially true for early and transitional level readers as well as English language learners (ELL) and children with all different learning styles. We've provided ideas for games and activities that can be varied to suit the needs of your group.

Personalized Sort Books

Student sort books are a good way to monitor student progress with word sorting while giving students a sense of ownership. You can make or purchase small notebooks for students to record sorts and complete follow-up challenges. For example, you could direct the student to draw a picture of another word that fits one of the categories.

Other follow-up work they record in the sort books could include word hunts and picture hunts (for picture representations of the word features in the sort). More advanced students could use sort words in a sentence. Sorting reinforcement activities that use language skills can be especially effective for ELL.

My Practice Space

in	id	ig	ip
bin	kid	pig	dip
tin	lid	dig	hip
fin	did	big	zip
pin	bid		lip
			tip

Activity Cards

Providing simply worded activity cards with instructions that include picture cues can make the word sort extension activities an even more independent ongoing

task. Be sure the students understand the activity before sending them to use task cards independently. And, of course, make sure the activities represent an appropriate level of challenge for every student. See page 97 for more Activity Card Reproducibles.

Speed Sort 1.
1. Put the category cards in a row.
2. Start a timer and sort the word cards.
3. When you are finished, stop the timer and record your time. Check the sort.
4. Sort the words again. Try to beat your time.

Speed Sort 2.
1. Put the category cards in a row.
2. Set a timer for _____ and start the timer.
3. Sort the words into the categories. When the time is up, stop and check the sort.
4. Record your score (number of words you sorted).
5. Repeat the speed sort. Try to beat your score.
Challenge

Games (matching word features or rhyming words):

See indicated pages for instructions and reproducibles.

- **Card Games** – play a version of Crazy 8's or Go Fish, matching word features (page 98)

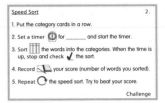

- **Board Games** – make word matches in order to progress along a path (page 37)
- **Word Cube Games** – name words that rhyme with words rolled on a cube (page 15)
- **Concentration** – make pairs by remembering the positions of words that share features such as rhymes or vowel sounds
- **Draw from a Hat** – take turns picking words and naming a matching word (page 8)
- **Word Baseball** – get a "base" in the classroom by correctly naming a word that matches a word feature shown on a flashcard

Activities:

See indicated pages for instructions and reproducibles.

- Activity Cards (page 147-150)
- Word Family Flip Book (page 15)
- Fortune Teller (page 152)
- Blank Sort Cards (page 145)
- Sorting Grid (page 146)

Related items to make or purchase:

- Magnetic sorts with lapboards
- Colorful Sorting Mats
- Word Family Cubes, sold with blank stickers
- Word Family Playing Cards
- Long Vowel Pattern Playing Cards
- My Sort Book (student sorting activity book)

Section I: Beginning Consonants Sounds Review

Use these beginning consonant sound sorts as a review and as a warm-up for more advanced word sorting.

Pictures are included on the category cards in this section only because students are still in the process of acquiring knowledge of letter-sound correspondence and benefit from the visual cues.

When to Use These Sorts
Your students already should have done extensive beginning sound study including picture sorting and phonemic awareness activities. These may have included sorting words with vowels in the beginning position; however, in preparation for sorting simple CVC words, students only need to sort by beginning consonants.

Reviewing Beginning Sounds
Start by contrasting sounds that can be elongated for emphasis, such as "mmm" for **m**, or easy sounds to hear such as /b/. At first, avoid comparing sounds that have the same place of articulation (how they feel in the mouth, where the air is pushed through) such as /t/ and /d/. Remember to provide repeated practice for beginning consonant sounds that students are using but confusing. Below is a demonstration sort for beginning sounds.

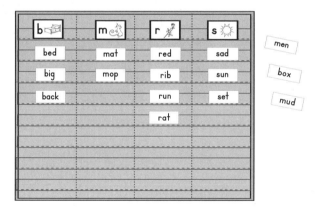

English Language Learners (ELL)
Spanish speakers might have confusion with consonant sounds that are pronounced differently or are not used in their native language. They may need extra practice with **g, h, j, k, v, w,** and **z**.

Once students can independently sort by beginning consonants and are correctly making letter-sound connections in their writing, you can move on to the next section of the book, Short Vowel Word Families.

Activity Idea: Student Activity Books

Have students keep personalized **word sort books** that include space for practicing and recording word sorts as well as space for reinforcement activities.

My Practice Space
pig

t	g	n	p
tag	gas	nap	pond
tip	gum	not	pig
tug	get	nip	pet
to	got	new	put
tell	good	nut	pan
ten	gill	nest	pop

Also, students can make **alphabet books** in which they write words and add pictures that start with the consonant sounds, one letter to a page. Consider having them make another book for ending sounds. Encourage students to cut out and glue pictures in their books as an alternative to drawing. Challenge them to use words other than the sort words.

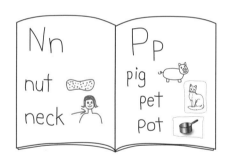

Students could also devote an entire **letter book** to one beginning sound:

Variations
- Have each group make a beginning sound book together.
- Require that the beginning sound words follow a theme (for example, animals).

Game Idea: Draw from a Hat

1. Gather a group of four to six students and assign a scorekeeper. Plan to supervise as necessary.
2. Place four to five letter cards for beginning sound categories in a row.
3. Place the word cards for the beginning sound categories in a hat or other container.
4. Players take turns drawing one word card, reading it aloud and placing it under the correct category card. They get a point each time they can correctly sort a word. When a player is not able to sort the word, the word card goes to the next player, who attempts to sort it. If that player chooses the correct category, he or she gets the point and gets to draw another card. If not, the next player gets to try, and so on.
5. Players continue sorting the words until the hat is empty.
6. Have the group check the sort together and reflect on the game.

Variations

- Play the game without points. Players put back cards they cannot correctly sort.
- Using a timer, give students only 5 to 10 seconds to complete their turn.

Other Game Ideas

Blind Sort (page 150)
Play a competitive team version of a blind sort in which students hear and then sort words.

Word Cube (page 153)
Write words with beginning sounds you have been sorting on the squares of a cube. Have students roll the cube and say another word with the same beginning sound. No words can be repeated. (See page 15 for instructions.)

Bingo (page 155)
Read words aloud and have students mark words with matching beginning sounds (for example, students hear a word that starts with /d/ and mark all the **d** words on their Bingo boards). The first student to fill a row (or the whole board if you're playing "Blackout") wins the round.

Word Hop Board Game (page 154)
Players advance along a simple game board by matching words that have the same beginning consonant sounds. (See page 37 for instructions.)

Beginning Consonant Sound Sorts	
#1	Beginning Sounds: **b, m, r, s**
#2	Beginning Sounds: **t, g, n, p**
#3	Beginning Sounds: **c, h, f, v**
#4	Beginning Sounds: **l, k, j, w**
#5	Beginning Sounds: **y, z, v**

bag	red	mop
mat	sob	bed
set	rib	rod
mud	back	mash
rat	mix	rest
sun	big	sad
men	sip	bus
box	run	sand

tag	pet	new
gas	to	put
nap	get	nut
pond	pig	gill
not	tell	nest
tip	got	pan
gum	nip	pop
tug	good	ten

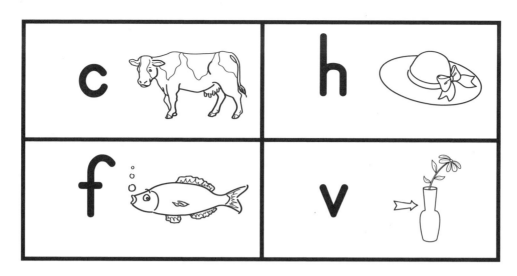

cup	hug	cub
hat	vest	fin
fat	fox	fish
hen	hot	vet
van	cot	fun
him	hand	vat
cost	fed	vast
vent	can	cat

lend	wax	went
wig	kin	lap
kit	wet	jet
leg	king	lid
kiss	win	just
jam	jog	lot
kid	word	lug
job	jump	kite

y 	z 	v
yam	yes	vent
zap	zig	zip
vet	your	yell
you	zag	vat
zest	van	yet
vest	zebra	very

Section II: Short Vowel Word Families

This section looks at simple spelling patterns in common short vowel word families. Use these sorts in conjunction with word building. Show that changing just the beginning sound in a word can make a new word that rhymes with it.

When to Use These Sorts

Your students already should have done plenty of picture and word sorting, mainly looking at the consonants in the beginning sound position.

Complete the sorts in the suggested order, making sure students are comfortable with sorting CVC words before asking them to sort CVCC, short vowel words that end in two consonants.

Activity Idea: Word Family Flip Books

1. Copy the *Word Family Flip Book Reproducible* (page 151) for each student.
2. The student writes a rime on the strip of paper and consonants that make words with that rime in the boxes. (Assign different rimes to represent various word families.)
3. The student cuts out the flip book, stacks the consonant cards on the left side of the rime strip and staples them along the left side.
4. The student practices making new short vowel words by flipping up the letters to reveal different beginning sounds.
5. Discuss how the students made word families by changing just the beginning sound, or onset.

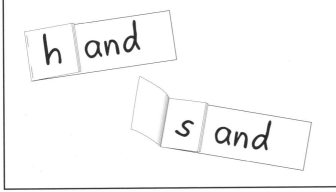

Game Idea: Word Cube

1. Copy the *Word Cube Reproducible* on page 153.
2. Fill in the spaces with word family words. Depending on how many word families you want to practice, you may include more than one word from each family.
3. Cut out the cube along the solid lines, fold along the dotted lines, and tape or glue it together.
4. Assign a scorekeeper.
5. The first player rolls the cube and reads the word that lands face up. If the player can name a word from the same word family, he or she gets one point. If not, the turn is over and the next player goes.
6. Play until one of the players reaches 10 points.

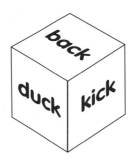

Variations
• Partners play against other teams, thinking of words together.
• Students working in a literacy center roll the cube and write as many words as they can within a time limit.
• Write just the rimes, not the complete words, on the cube.

Other Game Ideas

Word Family Card Game
Students take turns matching word family words in a game like Crazy 8's. See page 98 for card game instructions.

Word Family Fortune Tellers (page 152)
Construct a copy of the *Fortune Teller Reproducible* and fill in the spaces in the first two levels with word family words. Partners will get spelling practice by counting out words such as **bat** (b-a-t). The final flap could have a silly fortune, a joke or a quick task.

Draw from a Hat
Match word family words drawn from a hat or container. (See page 8 for detailed instructions.)

CVC Word Family Sorts
#6	CVC Word Families:	am, an, at, ad
#7	CVC Word Families:	ag, ap, ab
#8	CVC Word Families:	ed, en, et, eg
#9	CVC Word Families:	id, ig, in, ip
#10	CVC Word Families:	ob, op, ot, og
#11	CVC Word Families:	ug, un, ut, um
#12	CVC Word Families:	ap, ip, op
#13	CVC Word Families:	an, en, in, un
#14	CVC Word Families:	ad, ed, id
#15	CVC Word Families:	at, et, ot, ut
#16	CVC Word Families:	ag, ig, og, ug

CVCC Word Families
#17	CVCC Word Families:	ack, and, ash
#18	CVCC Word Families:	ell, end, ent, est
#19	CVCC Word Families:	ick, ill, ish, ist
#20	CVCC Word Families:	ock, og, ot
#21	CVCC Word Families:	uck, ump, unk, ust
#22	CVCC Word Families:	ist, est, ust
#23	CVCC Word Families:	and, end
#24	CVCC Word Families:	ack, uck, ick, ock
#25	CVCC Word Families:	ash, ish, ush

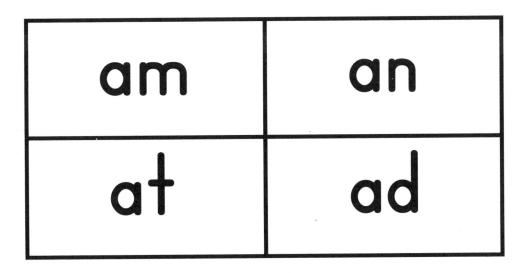

jam	ham	vat
ban	cat	dad
mat	mad	sad
tan	yam	Sam
dam	sat	can
pad	van	bad
pan	rat	man
bat	ram	had

ag	ap	ab
wag	tap	tab
cap	sap	sag
bag	cab	lab
nab	rag	map
nap	gap	lag
tag	dab	jab

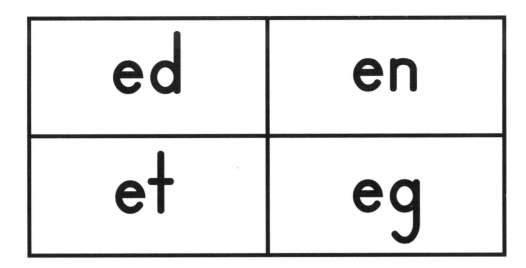

ed	en	
et	eg	

red	set	wet
men	bed	beg
led	met	Ted
ten	wed	then
Meg	pet	peg
hen	leg	pen
let	net	
fed	den	

id	ig
in	ip

rid	lip	pin
dig	fig	hip
zip	bin	wig
big	lid	win
bid	kin	fin
pig	did	sip
hid	tin	kid
rig	rip	dip

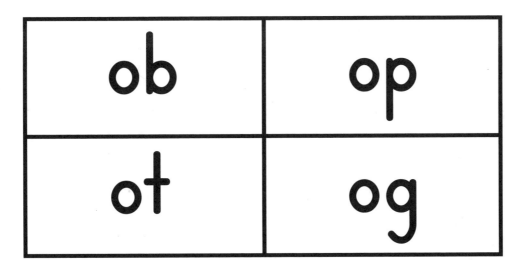

sob	hot	cob
log	job	hog
top	lot	cop
lob	rob	jog
pop	not	rot
mop	hop	bog
bop	pot	mob
got	dog	fog

ug	un
ut	um

tug	jug	hut
but	bug	run
nun	pun	rut
gut	rug	bun
cut	gum	nut
hum	dug	mug
fun	sun	
sum	hug	

ap	ip	op
nap	hip	hop
tip	zip	map
mop	top	lop
sap	gap	sip
dip	pop	cap
tap	rip	sop

an	en
in	un

run	tin	nun
can	den	Ben
men	pin	fun
van	hen	pan
ten	win	kin
bin	fin	pun
tan	bun	ban
pen	man	sun

ad	ed	id
hid	fed	Ned
pad	sad	bid
wed	led	mad
kid	dad	rid
red	bed	bad
lid	tad	did

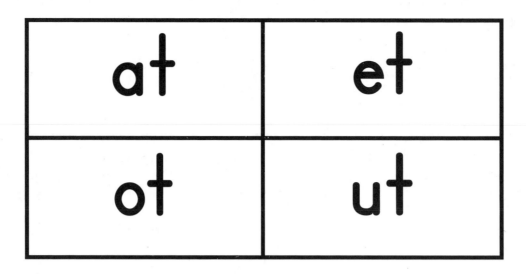

at	et
ot	ut

rut	hot	but
pot	met	gut
net	rat	wet
cat	cut	mat
bet	lot	hut
sat	not	pat
pet	let	nut
got	dot	bat

ag	ig
og	ug

dog	rig	dug
wig	jog	log
mug	fig	pig
rag	hog	rug
nag	tag	sag
dig	big	tug
wag	bog	bag
fog	bug	hug

ack	and	ash
rack	tack	back
dash	sand	grand
band	sack	lash
pack	mash	hand
sash	stand	shack
land	cash	rash

test	tell	rent
dent	mend	best
sell	sent	fell
lend	fend	rest
nest	bent	pest
shell	went	bell
bend	well	send
tend	lent	vest

ick	ill
ish	ist

lick	fist	swish
twist	fill	mist
pill	kick	list
dish	mill	will
sick	tick	pick
trick	fish	wrist
bill	drill	wish

ock	og	ot
jog	hog	sock
lock	clock	hot
not	log	frog
rock	pot	lot
dog	fog	block
dock	got	cot

uck	ump
unk	ust

hunk	duck	must
gust	dunk	puck
luck	dump	rust
bump	junk	hump
buck	suck	dust
tuck	trunk	pump
lump	jump	trust
bunk	sunk	just

ist	est	ust
gust	rust	fist
wrist	test	rest
best	dust	just
must	mist	nest
pest	vest	
list	bust	

and	end

band	sand	brand
blend	lend	send
land	hand	grand
mend	tend	bend

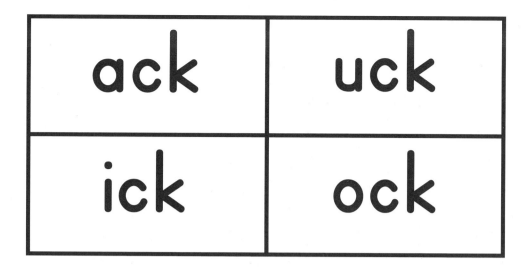

block	back	rock
rack	duck	wick
sick	pick	dock
suck	sack	Jack
tack	kick	sock
tick	luck	lock
crack	lick	tuck
buck	muck	knock

ash	ish	ush
mush	rush	dash
cash	mash	fish
dish	swish	bash
lash	rash	brush
wish	hush	lush

Section III: Blends and Digraphs

The sorts in this section look at the consonant blends and digraphs that appear at the beginning and ending of words.

When to Use These Sorts
At this point in their word work, your students already should have sorted plenty of words by beginning sound. Beginning blends and digraph sorts follow the same concept.

Teaching Blends and Digraphs
Start with digraphs, explaining that sometimes two consonants make a single sound, such as **ch**. First sort the two letters as separate beginning sounds along with words that start with the digraph.

For example, compare **c, h,** and **ch** with words like **cat, hat,** and **chat**. If you notice your students are still having trouble with the concept, continue splitting up digraphs this way before you start comparing the common digraphs to each other, such as **ch** words vs. **sh** words.

Note about th: We have included words that begin with both "voiced" and "unvoiced" **th**. Have students feel how their vocal chords vibrate when saying words like **the, that,** and **those** (voiced) and compare this to words such as **thin, thank,** and **thirteen** (unvoiced).

Once students understand digraphs, introduce blends following the same format. First explain that, unlike with digraphs, the two consonants can both still be heard in a blend. For example, in **flag**, you can hear both the **f** and the **l.**

Finally, sort words by ending digraphs and blends. Again, if you notice the concepts are too challenging, slow your pace and split up ending blends as necessary.

English Language Learners (ELL)
Remember that not all the blends and digraphs in English occur in other languages. Native Spanish speakers, for example, may need extra support with the digraphs they do not encounter in Spanish: **sh, th,** and **wh.**

Activity Idea: My Sort Book
Have students keep personalized word sort books that include space for practicing and recording word sorts as well as space for reinforcement activities.

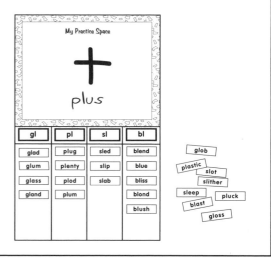

Game Idea: Word Hop Board Game

Use a simple game board to present a variety of matching and sorting challenges in a fun setting. You can make two copies of the reproducible Word Hop game board and tape them together for a larger board. Here is one example for a blend and digraph matching game.

1. Copy the *Word Hop Game Board Reproducible* from page 154.
2. Fill the spaces on a game board with category cards for a minimum of three different blend or digraph categories in random order, such as **sn, sk, sl, sn, sl, sk**. At first, use fewer categories, repeating as necessary to fill the game board and provide plenty of practice.
3. Gather and shuffle the word cards that fit all the categories and place them in a pile face down next to the game board. Let each player choose a colored game marker.
4. The first player flips a coin: tails means they get one "hop" and heads means two hops. The player moves the marker, reads the category aloud, and then draws a word card from the pile. If the word fits the category, the player places the word card

on top of the category card, and gets to take another turn. If the word does not fit the category, the player puts it in a discard pile.

5. Players make their way along the board until they reach the end. The first player to finish wins the game.

6. Have students review all the word cards to make sure they have been placed on the correct categories.

Variations

• Play an oral version in which students come up with words that match the categories and say them aloud. Supervision is recommended.

• Play with ending blends.

• Use word cards to indicate categories (for example, **skin** card means **sk** words go here).

Other Game Ideas

Word Cube (page 153)
Name another word with the same blend or digraph. (See instructions on page 15.)

Bingo (page 155)
Read words aloud and have students mark words with matching sound patterns (for example, student hears a short **i** word and marks all the short **i** words on their page).

Blend/Digraph Card Game
Write blend words on playing cards and have students play matching games such as "Go Fish."

Blends and Digraph Sorts

#26	Beginning Digraphs: **j, ch**		#54	Beginning Blends: **f, r, fr**
#27	Beginning Digraphs: **c, h, ch**		#55	Beginning Blends: **p, r, pr**
#28	Beginning Digraphs: **s, h, sh**		#56	Beginning Blends: **p, l, pl**
#29	Beginning Digraphs: **t, h, th**		#57	Beginning Blends: **c, l, cl**
#30	Beginning Digraphs: **w, h, wh**		#58	Beginning Blends: **c, r, cr**
#31	Beginning Digraphs: **ch, sh**		#59	Beginning Blends: **t, r, tr**
#32	Beginning Digraphs: **th** (unvoiced), **th** (voiced)		#60	Beginning Blends: **t, w, tw**
#33	Beginning Digraphs: **th, wh**		#61	Beginning Blends: **d, r, dr**
#34	Beginning Digraphs: **ch, sh, th, wh**		#62	Beginning Blends: **pl, pr**
#35	Beginning Blends: **s, t, st**		#63	Beginning Blends: **gl, gr**
#36	Beginning Blends: **s, p, sp**		#64	Beginning Blends: **cl, cr**
#37	Beginning Blends: **s, k, sk**		#65	Beginning Blends: **bl, br**
#38	Beginning Blends: **s, m, sm**		#66	Beginning Blends: **fl, fr**
#39	Beginning Blends: **s, n, sn**		#67	Beginning Blends: **tr, tw, qu**
#40	Beginning Blends: **s, l, sl**		#68	Beginning Blends: **gl, pl, sl, bl**
#41	Beginning Blends: **s, w, sw**		#69	Beginning Blends: **dr, gr, cr, br**
#42	Beginning Blends: **s, c, sc**		#70	Beginning Blends: **gr, gl, cr, cl**
#43	Beginning Blends: **sp, st**		#71	Beginning Blends: **br, bl, pr, pl**
#44	Beginning Blends: **sk, sm**		#72	Ending Digraphs: **_ch, _sh, _th, _ss**
#45	Beginning Blends: **st, sp, sk, sm**		#73	Ending Blends: **_sk, _sp, _st**
#46	Beginning Blends: **sn, sl**		#74	Ending Blends: **_ft, _pt, _lt, _st**
#47	Beginning Blends: **sw, sc**		#75	Ending Blends: **_lf, _lp, _lk _lt**
#48	Beginning Blends: **sn, sl, sw, sc**		#76	Ending Blends (Preconsonantal Nasals): **_m, _p, _mp**
#49	Beginning Blends: **g, l, gl**		#77	Ending Blends (Preconsonantal Nasals): **_n, _d, _nd**
#50	Beginning Blends: **g, r, gr**		#78	Ending Blends (Preconsonantal Nasals): **_n, _k, _ng**
#51	Beginning Blends: **b, r, br**		#79	Ending Blends (Preconsonantal Nasals): **_n, _g, _nk**
#52	Beginning Blends: **b, l, bl**		#80	Ending Blends (Preconsonantal Nasals): **_n, _t, _nt**
#53	Beginning Blends: **f, l, fl**		#81	Ending Blends (Preconsonantal Nasals): **_mp, _nd, _nt**
			#82	Ending Blends (Preconsonantal Nasals): **_nk, _ng**

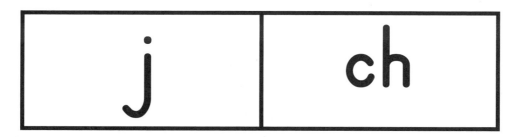

j		
chop	jet	junk
jam	chat	jeans
chick	job	chip
jab	check	cheese

c	h	ch

chin	cop	check
cat	chunk	cap
hat	hog	his
cub	cup	cot
hop	chat	him
chick	hunk	chop

s	h	sh
hut	sold	shut
sip	hip	sort
shell	shape	help
hop	sun	ship
sand	house	hat
short	sell	shop

t	h	th
thirteen	hand	top
horn	tick	hat
tin	thorn	thirty
has	him	turkey
thick	torn	hop
tail	thing	thin

w	h	wh
where	we	whip
wish	hip	hill
hum	hand	west
word	which	when
will	wash	why
hen	hope	whisper

ch	sh

chop	ship	short
check	shop	chin
shape	chick	she
chunk	shut	chip

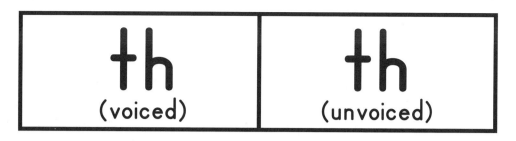

th (voiced)		th (unvoiced)
thick	the	they
thirteen	thorn	then
thump	there	thank
that	thin	this

th	wh

think	when	why
thirty	thick	where
whip	which	thin
thirteen	thank	whisper

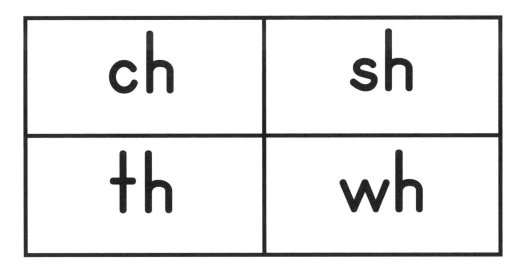

where	check	when
chunk	think	shut
thirty	shell	which
chick	thick	chop
she	short	why
shin	thirteen	ship
thin	whip	chip
thank	chin	whisper

s	t	st
sand	stop	tunnel
top	sun	sing
stand	sting	tan
sop	sad	tick
stun	tart	stick
toss	sick	start

s	p	sp
spell	pin	puck
sell	spot	pit
pot	pill	spin
sick	sin	some
spun	pal	spill
sap	suck	spit

s	k	sk

s	k	sk
skeleton	sip	kit
set	skit	sand
kill	keep	kiss
sit	sunk	skip
skunk	skin	king
kin	sad	skill

s	m	sm
sell	soggy	smack
mall	monkey	met
smoke	sun	sash
sick	smell	must
miss	sack	small
smoggy	mash	smash

s	n	sn
set	so	snake
neck	now	nail
snicker	sun	no
sick	snail	sail
nickel	sack	nut
sneak	sniff	snack

s	l	sl
sip	slot	sack
slack	sap	lack
lap	led	slip
sob	such	lick
slick	lot	sick
lip	sled	slap

s	w	sw
wag	song	west
sell	wish	swim
swift	suck	well
sing	sweet	swish
wig	sag	sift
swing	wing	swell

S	C	SC
could	core	sack
scooter	scan	sat
sell	sore	cab
cub	cut	can
scurry	score	scuffle
sick	such	scab

sp	st

spot	spun	spell
stand	stop	sting
spill	spit	spin
stick	stun	steal

sk	sm

smooth	skate	smell
skit	small	skin
smash	sketch	smoke
skill	skunk	smack

sting	smooth	stick
spun	stop	skit
sketch	skunk	spot
small	spill	spawn
start	smash	skip
spur	step	smell
stand	spin	smoke
skeleton	smack	skin

sn	sl

sneak	slip	slick
slot	snail	snack
snicker	snake	sloppy
slap	sled	sniff

SW	SC

swim	scale	swell
score	swish	scan
swing	sweet	scooter
scab	scold	swam

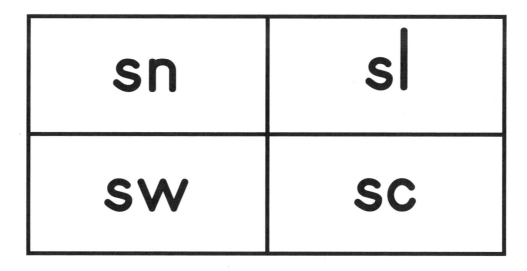

sn	sl
sw	sc

snitch	swish	snack
slip	scan	swing
swam	sniff	scuffle
scurry	sled	sweet
snicker	snake	score
slot	swim	sloppy
snail	slap	scooter
slick	swell	scab

g	l	gl
good	glass	gum
little	go	lend
gloss	land	glum
gift	gap	lob
gland	loss	glad
luck	glob	gob

g	r	gr
runt	gram	grunt
grass	got	gash
gum	red	rip
rash	gab	rock
grab	get	grand
go	ram	grip

b	r	br
bred	rush	bed
rag	rock	rent
band	brand	brush
bond	bag	brag
bring	ring	branch
ranch	boss	red

b	l	bl
band	bond	back
black	bland	bed
land	led	list
last	bend	lack
blush	blond	bled
lend	big	blend

f	l	fl

flip	lag	fox
fat	fill	flag
luck	flash	fun
fish	lick	lip
lost	fan	lash
flat	flush	flesh

f	r	fr
far	fish	rash
fret	rub	fog
rent	frog	frost
fix	fan	full
rag	fresh	rock
French	rip	frock

p	r	pr
pack	pick	pry
prim	press	rent
ran	red	rim
pencil	pop	print
problem	puff	pan
rock	rash	prick

p	l	pl
lamb	puck	pot
plump	luck	lit
pant	plant	plot
lot	pump	let
pan	lump	plan
pluck	pet	plus

c	l	cl
can	cub	come
clash	luck	list
lash	class	club
cob	cash	lip
lock	cut	less
clip	clock	click

c	r	cr
rash	cut	cop
cab	run	rack
rest	cash	crash
cot	crest	rot
crack	cup	crab
crib	rib	crop

t	r	tr
rip	test	tick
rot	trash	rest
trick	tip	tuck
tack	trip	rack
truck	rug	trot
rash	tug	track

t	w	tw

tap	would	twig
twitch	tin	tell
witch	twin	twirl
ten	wag	tunnel
wig	top	win
twist	wet	twelve

d	r	dr
drink	dirt	drop
dam	draft	down
dim	rest	do
rag	duck	raft
dress	drag	rob
rink	rip	drip

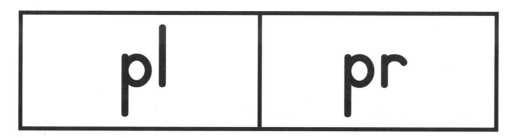

pry	plot	plus
plant	princess	plump
prop	pluck	press
plan	print	prick

gl	gr

glass	grunt	glum
grow	glob	gram
grass	gland	grab
glad	grip	glossy

cl	cl	cr
clap	click	crowd
club	crack	class
crash	crab	crust
clip	clock	crib

bl	br

bran	blot	brush
bled	blank	bland
brick	brag	black
blend	bride	bread

flash	flag	fresh
free	flip	frost
frill	frog	flush
flesh	fluff	France

tr	tw	qu
quiz	twin	quack
track	twist	truck
trash	trip	quick
twelve	twirl	train
quit	twice	twig
trot	quail	question

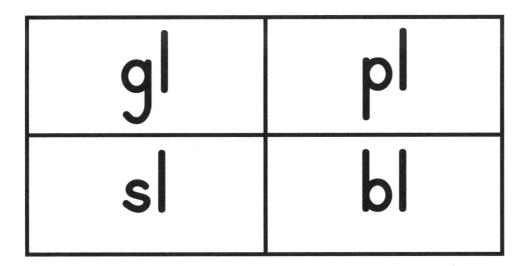

plug	plod	blue
glad	slip	pluck
sled	gloss	bliss
gland	slab	glob
blend	slot	blond
glum	slither	plastic
plenty	plum	blush
glass	sleep	blast

dr	gr
cr	br

crash	drum	grass
drip	grab	crib
grow	bran	crowd
dress	crack	brag
bridge	drop	brush
crab	grip	crust
drink	brick	bread
grand	grunt	drag

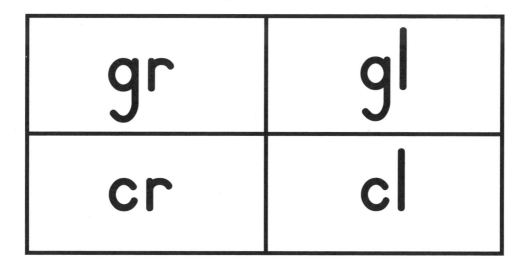

gr	gl
cr	cl

glen	glass	cross
grill	glob	clam
craft	cram	click
grab	crib	clog
class	grand	grim
grip	crash	clot
glance	grass	club
crisp	glad	gloss

br	bl
pr	pl

plug	blond	please
brick	blast	blush
broth	print	pluck
black	brown	prince
prod	prick	plot
bliss	press	branch
brush	plan	blend
prop	bridge	plump

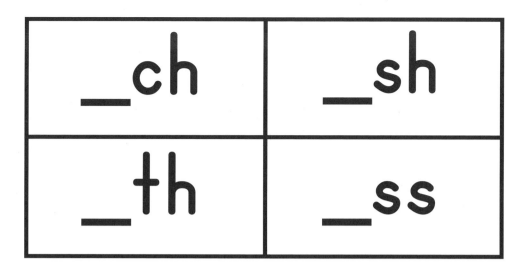

beach	push	sloth
fuss	rush	cash
which	reach	tooth
moth	such	pass
sandwich	dash	kiss
miss	with	dress
wish	fish	teach
bath	math	guess

_sk	_sp	_st
just	dusk	wasp
mask	crisp	fast
lisp	musk	desk
task	wisp	ask
last	gasp	wrist
cusp	cast	west

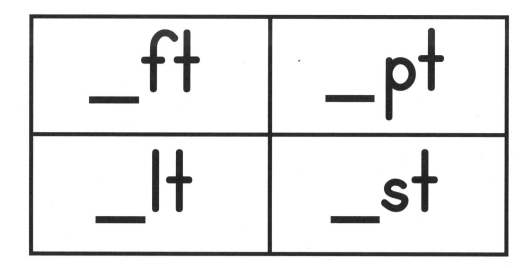

fast	slept	last
loft	wilt	bolt
craft	swept	drift
adapt	colt	cast
west	erupt	adult
kept	felt	just
lift	soft	draft
wept	melt	wrist

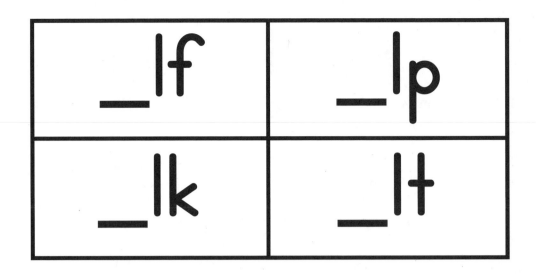

talk	gulp	wilt
help	milk	half
self	pulp	kelp
golf	chalk	bolt
silk	elf	shelf
felt	walk	colt
scalp	yelp	calf
melt	bulk	adult

_m	_p	_mp
camp	slim	stomp
am	chimp	gum
chop	sap	gap
gem	lamp	dam
pump	from	grip
cup	top	stump

_n	_d	_nd
pond	son	bed
pen	pod	mud
kid	end	Chad
hen	chin	and
blend	kind	than
bad	soon	wind

_n	_k	_nk
son	peek	chin
beak	bunk	pink
fun	week	cheek
book	than	tank
thank	hen	think
look	honk	pen

_n	_g	_ng
long	win	wing
van	tag	ten
pin	hung	drug
bring	drag	sang
ran	wig	man
bag	hug	thing

_n	_t	_nt
but	chin	out
hen	mint	ant
front	get	pen
son	soon	went
knit	bat	than
hunt	lit	spent

_mp	_nd	_nt
lamp	chimp	stomp
and	kind	mint
band	front	stump
ant	wind	hunt
pump	pond	camp
blend	lent	spent

_nk	_ng

thank	wing	long
bunk	think	bring
sang	hung	honk
pink	tank	thing

Section IV: Short, Long and R-Controlled Vowel Sorts

Now your students are ready to study spelling patterns that make a vowel sound short or long as well as common exceptions to those patterns.

When to Use These Sorts
Up to this point your students have encountered vowel sounds in rhyming CVC and CVCC short vowel word families, but have not yet studied them in isolation. Now they will listen for vowel sounds as they recognize the patterns they have already examined in word family sorts. They will see that word features help determine if a vowel sound is going to be short, long, or a variation such as **r**-controlled.

Complete the sorts in the suggested order. Once your students have mastered the last of these word features, the **r**-controlled vowels, they will be ready to sort by diphthongs, complex consonant clusters, inflectional endings such as **-ed** and **-ing**, and so on.

Sequence of These Sorts
At first your students will compare short vowel sounds that are easier to distinguish, such as **short a** vs. **short o** and **short i** vs. **short u**. As students progress through the word sorts and begin to show understanding of short vowels, your word sorting should focus on less obvious sound distinctions such as **short e** vs. **short i**.

Note about long vowel patterns: As it was our intention with this section to introduce the most common long vowel patterns, less common patterns such as **e_e** (long **e** with silent **e** at the end) have been omitted. You can add this and other long vowel categories if you'd like, using blank sort cards (see page 145).

"Other" Words
Many high frequency words do not follow the familiar pronunciation rules that would usually indicate a short or long vowel sound.

Use the **other** category to show clear exceptions to the spelling patterns (for example, **was** is a CVC word that does not make a short **a** sound). Or, if appropriate for your group, use it for less obvious distinctions. For example, include **was** in a **short u** vs. **short a** sort, and challenge students to notice that **was** makes a **short u** sound.

Note: This is a good time to talk about different pronunciations based on regional accents or students' native languages. This may come up in decisions students make when sorting.

English Language Learners (ELL)
Remember, for students who are not native English speakers, short and long vowel sounds can be a whole new concept. In Spanish, for example, every vowel or diphthong (vowel combination such as **ue** in **pueblo**) is pronounced just one way; letter-sound correspondence is regular.

Activity Idea: Student Activity Cards
The student follows instructions that call for completing a sort and then records the sort and a follow-up activity in a personalized sort book or notebook. This can also be a place for reflecting on the sort in writing.

Copy pages 147 to 150, Activity Card Reproducibles. The easier version of the activity goes on one side of the card and the "challenge" goes on the other side. We recommend using color to distinguish the challenge side. An icon in the lower left corner of some cards indicates a partner activity.

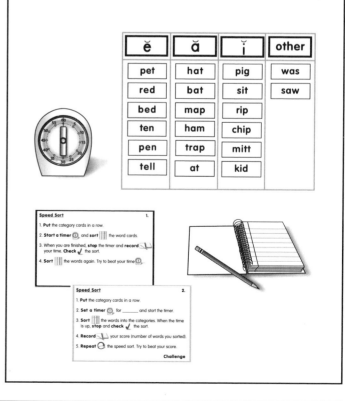

97

Game Idea: Long Vowel Pattern Card Game

Using groups of four words in four different colors, you can play matching games similar to Crazy 8's or Go Fish!

1. Purchase or make playing cards showing long vowel pattern words, four colored cards per pattern. For example, came = blue, sale = yellow, take = red, gate = green; pain = blue, wait = yellow, sail = red, stain = green; and so on). Also include one or two Wild Cards.

2. Shuffle the cards and give each player five cards. The remaining cards go face down in a pile. Turn over the top card and place it face up next to the pile.

3. The first player checks their hand for a card that matches either the long vowel pattern or the color. If the player has a match, they place the card on top of the matching card face up and the turn is over. If not, the player must draw cards until there is a match. Wild Cards can be used to represent any long vowel pattern or color.

4. The first player to run out of cards wins the game.

Variations

- Decrease competition level by making everyone a winner; the first player to go out teams up with the player who's ahead.
- Whenever a certain color is played, everyone must keep quiet until the color is changed.

Other Game Ideas

Word Cube (page 153)
Name another word with the same vowel sound or pattern. (See page 15 for instructions.)

Bingo (page 155)
Read words aloud and have students mark words with matching sound patterns (for example, student hears a short i word and marks all the short i words on their page).

Word Hop Board Game (page 154)
Players advance along a simple game board by matching words that have the same vowel sound or pattern. (See page 37 for instructions.)

Short, Long and R-Controlled Vowel Sorts
Short Vowels
#83 Short Vowels: ă, ŏ
#84 Short Vowels: ă, ŏ, other
#85 Short Vowels: ĭ, ŭ
#86 Short Vowels: ĭ, ŭ, other
#87 Short Vowels: ĕ, ă, ĭ
#88 Short Vowels: ĕ, ă, ĭ, other
#89 Short Vowels: ă, ĕ, ĭ, ŏ, ŭ
#90 Short Vowels: ă, ĕ, ĭ, ŏ, ŭ, other
#91 Short Vowels with Beginning Digraphs: ă, ĕ, ĭ, ŏ, ŭ
#92 Short Vowels with Beginning Digraphs: ă, ĕ, ĭ, ŏ, ŭ, other
#93 Short Vowels with Beginning Blends: ă, ĕ, ĭ, ŏ, ŭ
#94 Short Vowels with Beginning Blends: ă, ĕ, ĭ, ŏ, ŭ, other
#95 Short Vowels with Ending Digraphs: ă, ĕ, ĭ, ŏ, ŭ
#96 Short Vowels with Ending Blends: ă, ĕ, ĭ, ŏ, ŭ

Short and Long Vowels
#97 Short and Long Vowels: ă, ā
#98 Short and Long Vowels: ă, ā, other
#99 Short and Long Vowels: ĭ, ī
#100 Short and Long Vowels: ĭ, ī, other
#101 Short and Long Vowels: ŏ, ō
#102 Short and Long Vowels: ŏ, ō, other
#103 Short and Long Vowels: ŭ, ū
#104 Short and Long Vowels: ŭ, ū, other
#105 Short and Long Vowels Review: CVC, CVCe, other

Short and Long Vowel Patterns
#106 Short & Long Vowel Patterns: ă (CVC), ā (CVCe), ā (CVVC)
#107 Short & Long Vowel Patterns: ă (CVC), ā (CVCe), ā (CVVC), other
#108 Short & Long Vowel Patterns: ŏ (CVC), ō (CVCe), ō (CVVC)
#109 Short and Long Vowel Patterns: ŏ (CVC), ō (CVCe), ō (CVVC), other
#110 Short & Long Vowel Patterns: ŭ (CVC), ū (CVCe), ōō, (CVVC), ūī (CVVC)
#111 Short & Long Vowel Patterns: ŭ (CVC), ū (CVCe), ū (CVVC), other
#112 Short & Long Vowel Patterns: ĕ (CVC), ēā (CVVC), ēē (CVVC)
#113 Short & Long Vowel Patterns: ĕ (CVC), ēā (CVVC), ēē (CVVC), other

Common Long Vowel Patterns
#114 Long Vowel Patterns (a): ai, oa, ee, ea
#115 Long Vowel Patterns (a): ay, ai, a_e
#116 Long Vowel Patterns (a): ei, ey
#117 Long Vowel Patterns (e): e, ee, ea
#118 Long Vowel Patterns (i): i_e, igh, y
#119 Long Vowel Patterns (o): oa, ow
#120 Long Vowel Patterns (u): ue, ew, oo

R-Controlled Vowels
#121 R-Controlled Vowels: or, er
#122 R-Controlled Vowels: ir, ar, ur
#123 R-Controlled Vowels Review: or, er, ir, ar, ur

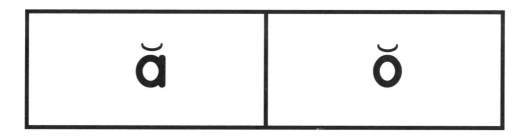

rag	top	bad
jam	dog	nod
at	on	tap
van	not	job

ă	ŏ	other
log	saw	ton
pan	nod	of
that	as	all
pot	shot	mad
am	mop	
job	ran	

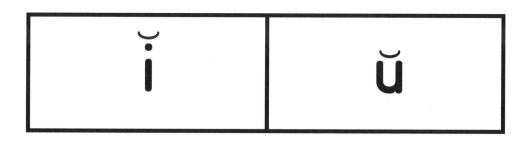

ĭ	ŭ	
win	fun	but
big	rip	mud
hill	up	it
rug	kid	cub

ĭ	ŭ	other
mitt	put	run
fish	in	fun
dip	nut	rub
bus	kit	
is	bug	

ĕ	ă	ĭ
van	bad	rip
win	an	rag
bed	led	then
net	at	if
tap	sit	set
sell	kid	hill

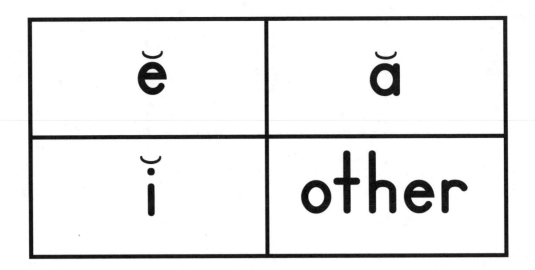

ĕ	ă
ĭ	other

kid	bat	tell
bed	at	chip
pen	trap	sit
pig	ham	saw
ten	mitt	pet
hat	map	was
red	rip	

ă	ĕ	ĭ
ŏ	ŭ	

bus	beg	lip
sad	tan	top
drop	hop	tell
big	tag	hot
that	pet	run
set	fill	tub
ram	red	fun
hut	dish	
dog	win	

ă	ĕ	ĭ
ŏ	ŭ	other

shut	pin	long
pan	rat	box
pod	shed	log
fig	mask	bud
had	put	sell
ten	peg	rug
mud	led	wish
pot	kit	mug
bag	tip	ton

ă	ě	ĭ
ŏ	ŭ	

chat	than	shell
thump	shelf	chocolate
shop	shed	chug
chap	when	shut
chill	thin	chip
chest	shock	wham
thumb	chop	thud
sham	whip	
ship	shot	

ă	ě	ĭ
ŏ	ŭ	other

thud	that	shock
shop	chill	thin
thick	than	chomp
shack	shell	shut
when	them	chest
wham	shift	chunk
thump	check	shot
chat	chick	thunder
chop	what	

ă	ĕ	ĭ
ŏ	ŭ	

gram	plot	frog
flush	flap	cross
sled	step	drop
drill	trap	club
skin	grill	crept
truck	class	drum
fresh	smell	pluck
flop	flip	
clam	bring	

ă	ĕ	ĭ
ŏ	ŭ	other

blend	dress	flip
skin	flash	stomp
drop	drill	frost
club	brag	plot
swat	plum	crop
grab	flag	brush
trust	bred	step
crash	press	drum
grip	crib	

ă	ĕ	ĭ
ŏ	ŭ	

muçh	moth	rich
cloth	bath	broth
mash	slosh	gosh
dash	trash	crush
fresh	mesh	flesh
which	math	rush
fish	with	wish
hush	Beth	such

ă	ĕ	ĭ
ŏ	ŭ	

lamp	must	soft
frost	past	test
bulk	pond	risk
pink	limp	send
ask	desk	lift
belt	blast	lost
trust	jump	stump
left	honk	
tilt	sand	

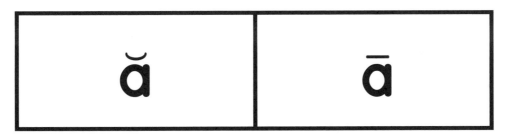

fade	cap	fad
plan	plane	cape
made	tape	rag
tap	mad	rage

ă	ā	other
pane	can	have
made	tap	cap
all	cane	plane
plan	mad	tape
cape	pan	what

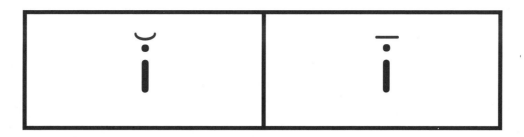

rid	fine	hide
shine	pin	slid
slide	ride	shin
hid	fin	pine

ĭ	ī	other
bit	pill	trip
bite	chime	mine
hid	fish	pile
like	white	live
give	hip	

nose	mole	job
hop	sock	hope
hose	clock	code
not	note	cod

ŏ	ō	other
hop	code	rod
note	some	hope
flop	clock	joke
love	rode	mole
sock	hot	come

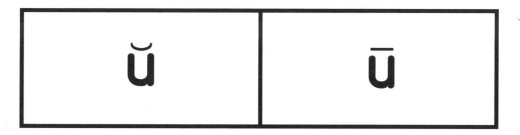

June	cub	tub
hug	cube	gut
jump	cut	flute
cute	huge	tube

ŭ	ū	other
cute	drum	hush
truck	huge	flute
put	hug	rule
jump	cut	
tube	tune	

CVC	CVCe	other
one	mad	plane
plan	hide	hope
have	rag	hid
hop	made	rage
come	cut	cute

ă (CVC)	ā (CVCe)	ā (CVVC)
tap	train	take
mail	trash	came
map	same	space
can	paint	pale
wag	tape	brain
trail	rain	
gas	make	

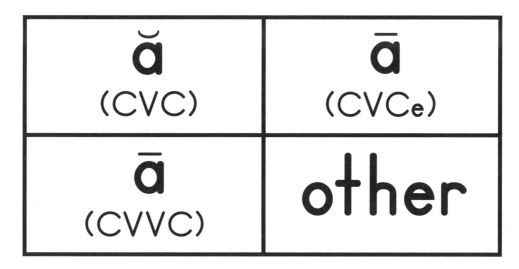

sand	sail	grain
paint	male	trace
said	had	cape
camp	cap	tame
pail	chain	rail
trap	chase	what
yam	race	have

Ŏ (CVC)	Ō (CVVe)	Ō (CVVC)
toast	chop	stone
mop	soft	croak
shot	toad	chose
moan	cross	rose
boat	mole	nose
drop	hole	soak

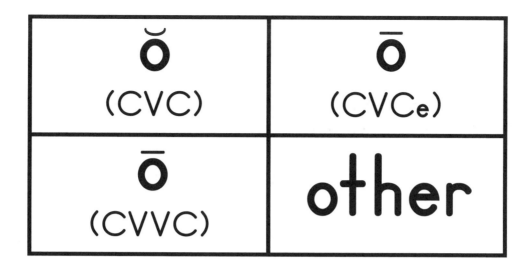

coal	goal	role
hope	lost	those
top	soap	got
coach	cost	home
dog	goat	come
foam	none	joke
frog	hole	

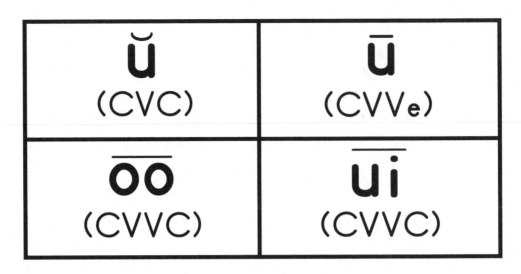

cut	cruise	moon
soon	crust	tube
fun	food	use
cartoon	trust	mule
run	cute	suit
tooth	fruit	juice
shut	flute	bruise
stool	cube	

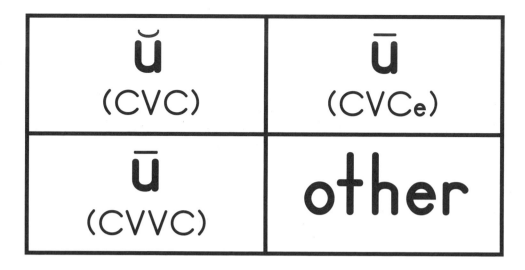

gum	shut	cute
tube	foot	June
up	huge	put
tooth	stool	food
cub	flute	plum
thumb	soon	cartoon
moon	cube	

ĕ (CVC)	ēa (CVVC)	ēe (CVVC)
feet	yell	tea
creep	feel	dream
bell	eat	shell
deep	yes	cheap
red	seal	net
teeth	leap	sleep

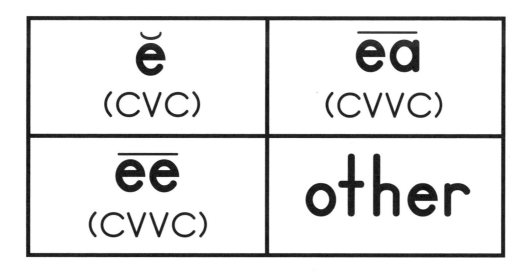

bed	meat	meet
sheet	men	best
seed	heat	sheep
leg	seat	bread
green	bean	tell
nest	meal	head
read	sweet	

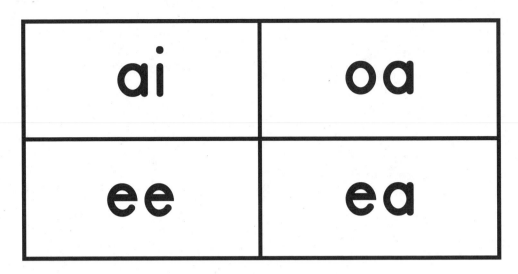

meat	mail	seed
paint	toad	read
moan	boat	croak
sweet	green	heat
brain	train	sheep
bean	meet	seat
trail	toast	rain
soak	sheet	meal

ay	ai	a_e
day	may	wait
whale	came	bake
brain	stay	laid
lay	paint	gate
pale	clay	way
trail	mail	ape

ei	ey

eight	sleigh	they
grey	hey	weigh
neighbor	vein	whey
their	prey	

e	ee	ea
be	mean	we
cheap	he	need
cheek	free	see
me	she	wheat
steal	tree	bead
feet	beat	

i_e	igh	y
shy	pile	bite
mine	my	sight
bright	white	fly
chime	high	night
by	like	sigh
light	sky	cry

oa	ow

boat	blow	crow
show	float	moan
grow	mow	roast
coat	loaf	know

ue	ew	oo
blue	stool	new
balloon	glue	hue
crew	blew	grew
tooth	clue	moon
chew	food	drew
true	due	soon

or	er

perk	for	herd
or	fern	corn
germ	fork	horn
term	born	her

ir	ar	ur
surf	sir	dirt
bird	turn	card
art	park	girl
third	stir	yard
purr	burn	fur
arm	far	hurt

or	er	ir
ar	ur	

north	curve	bark
slurp	merge	shark
twirl	over	are
storm	stern	nurse
were	chirp	curb
sport	thirty	world
first	start	blur
morning	shirt	
clerk	chart	

Date: _____

Dear Parent or Guardian:

In class we have been sorting words in order to see patterns and spell words automatically. Soon we will begin the _____ word sorts. I will be assigning sorts for your child to complete at home. Family members are encouraged to provide assistance when needed.

Word Sort

The child cuts up the cards and reads all the words. The word sorts include category cards showing word features, which the child places at the top of the desk to label the categories in columns.

The child reads each word aloud and places it under the category it matches. Guide the child in sorting any trouble words and then check the sort. Reflect on the sort together and write any comments below before signing your name.

b	m	r	s
bed	mat	red	sad
big	mop	rib	sun
back		run	set
		rat	

men
box
mud

Beginning Sounds #1

b	m
r	s

bag	red	mop
mat	sob	bed
set	rib	rod
mud	back	mash
rat	mix	rest
sun	big	sad
men	sip	bus
box	run	sand

We will be doing some variations of this activity including:
- **Speed sort** – word sort is timed
- **Blind sort** – student hears words and points to the categories
- **Open sort** – student sorts words into categories he or she chooses
- **Partner sort** – partners help each other complete the sort

Note: Some of the vowel sound sorts also include a category for exceptions, called "other."

Your support is always appreciated.

Sincerely,

_____

Student's name _____

Signature of parent or guardian

_____   Date _____

Fecha:_____

Estimados Padres o Guardián:

Para aprender a deletrear y leer palabras automáticamente, su hijo/a está haciendo unas actividades de clasificación en las que tiene que fijarse en los patrones y las letras de palabras. Ahora estamos estudiando palabras con _____. La tarea será clasificar palabras adentro de categorías distintas.

La Clasificación de Palabras

El/La estudiante recorta las tarjetas y lee todas las palabras. En cada actividad, hay tarjetas claves que nombran las categorías, y éstas deberían estar colocadas encima de cada columna.

El/La estudiante lee cada palabra en voz alta y la coloca debajo de la categoría que corresponde. Cuando sea necesario, le podría ayudar a clasificar la palabra y revisar el trabajo completo. Habla con su hijo/a acerca del trabajo y anota los comentarios en el espacio abajo antes de firmar su nombre.

Haremos varias actividades de clasificación distintas incluyendo:
- **Speed sort** – el/la estudiante clasifica las palabras dentro de un tiempo determinado
- **Blind sort** – el/la estudiante escucha una palabra y apunta a la categoría correcta
- **Open sort** – el/la estudiante clasifica las palabras según sus propias categorías
- **Partner sort** – se hace la clasificación en pareja

Ojo: Algunas actividades de vocales tienen una categoría para excepciones, llamada "otra" o en inglés, "other."

Gracias por su apoyo.

Sinceramente,

_____

Nombre de estudiante _____

Firma de los padres o guardián

_____   Fecha _____

Word Sort Record Sheet

Student or Group_____

Section I
Beginning Sounds

1	2	3	4	5

Beginning Consonant Sounds

Comments_____

_____

_____

Section II
Short Vowel Word Families

6	7	8	9	10	11	12	13	14	15	16

CVC Words

Comments_____

_____

_____

17	18	19	20	21	22	23	24	25

CVCC Words

Comments_____

_____

_____

Section III
Blends and Digraphs

26	27	28	29	30	31	32	33	34

Beginning Digraphs

Comments_____

_____

_____

35	36	37	38	39	40	41	42	43	44	45
46	47	48	49	50	51	52	53	54	55	56
57	58	59	60	61	62	63	64	65	66	67
68	69	70	71							

Beginning Blends

Comments_____

_____

_____

72	73	74	75	76	77	78	79	80	81	82

Ending Digraphs and Blends

Comments_____

_____

_____

_____

Section IV
Short, Long, and R-Controlled Vowels

83	84	85	86	87	88	89
90	91	92	93	94	95	96

Short Vowels

Comments_____

_____

_____

97	98	99	100	101	102	103	104	105

Short and Long Vowels (CVC/CVCC, CVCe)

Comments_____

_____

_____

106	107	108	109	110	111	112	113

Short and Long Vowel Patterns

Comments_____

_____

_____

114	115	116	117	118	119	120

Common Long Vowel Patterns

Comments_____

_____

_____

121	122	123

R-Controlled Vowels

Comments_____

_____

_____

145

Speed Sort

1.

1. **Put** the category cards in a row.

2. **Start a timer** and **sort** the word cards.

3. When you are finished, **stop** the timer and **record** your time. **Check** ✔ the sort.

4. **Sort** the words again. Try to beat your time .

Speed Sort

2.

1. **Put** the category cards in a row.

2. **Set a timer** for _____ and start the timer.

3. **Sort** the words into the categories. When the time is up, **stop** and **check** ✔ the sort.

4. **Record** your score (number of words you sorted).

5. **Repeat** ↻ the speed sort. Try to beat your score.

Challenge

Open Sort

1.

1. **Read** every word card.

2. **Sort** the cards into any categories you see.

3. **Write** a sentence about how you chose your categories.

Open Sort

2.

1. **Read** every word card.

2. **Sort** the cards into any letter or sound categories you see.

3. **Write** a sentence about how you chose your categories.

Challenge

Partner Sort

1.

1. With your partner **put** the category cards in a row.

2. **Split up** the word cards and take turns **sorting** them.

3. **Check** ✔ the sort together.

Partner Sort

2.

1. **Put** the category cards in a row.

2. **Split up** the word cards.

3. **Start a timer** and take turns **sorting** 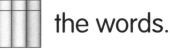 the words.

4. When you are finished, **record** your time and **check** ✔ the sort.

5. **Sort** the words again. Try to beat your time .

Challenge

Blind Sort   1.

1. **Put** the category cards in a row.

2. **Read** each word aloud and have your partner point to the category it fits.

3. **Repeat** the sort. This time, point to the category as your partner reads each word aloud.

Blind Sort   2.

1. **Help** your partner put the category cards in a row.

2. **Read** each word aloud and have your partner write the word below its category card.

3. **Repeat** the sort. This time, write each word as your partner reads it aloud.

Challenge

Write a rime on the long strip of paper (leaving space at the beginning) and consonants that make words with the rime in the smaller boxes. Cut out the boxes and stack the consonant cards on the left side of the rime strip. Staple along the left side to create the Flip Book.

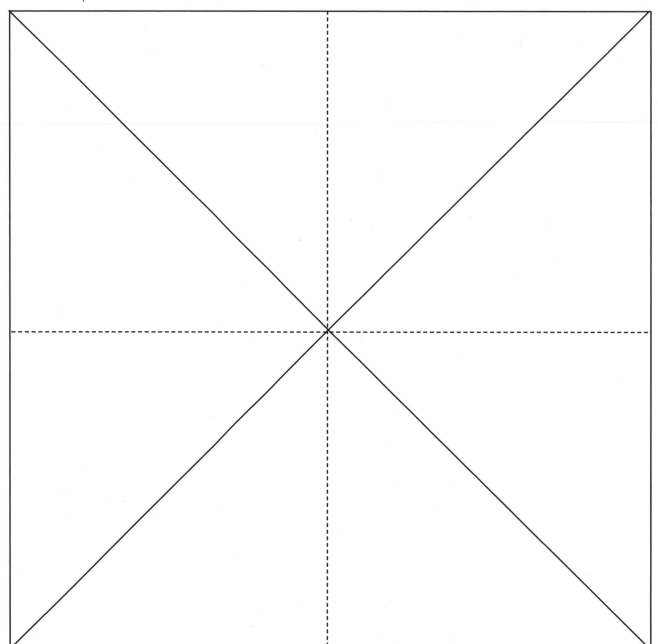

1. Fold each corner so it meets in the middle.

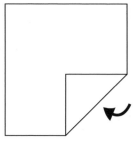

2. Turn Fortune over.

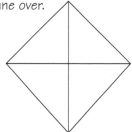

3. Fold each corner up again so it meets in the middle.

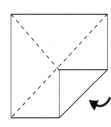

4. Fortune should look like this.

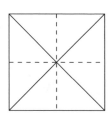

5. Fold the top over towards you.

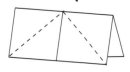

6. Place your fingers under the flaps. Move your fingers back and forth to open and close your fortune.

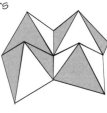

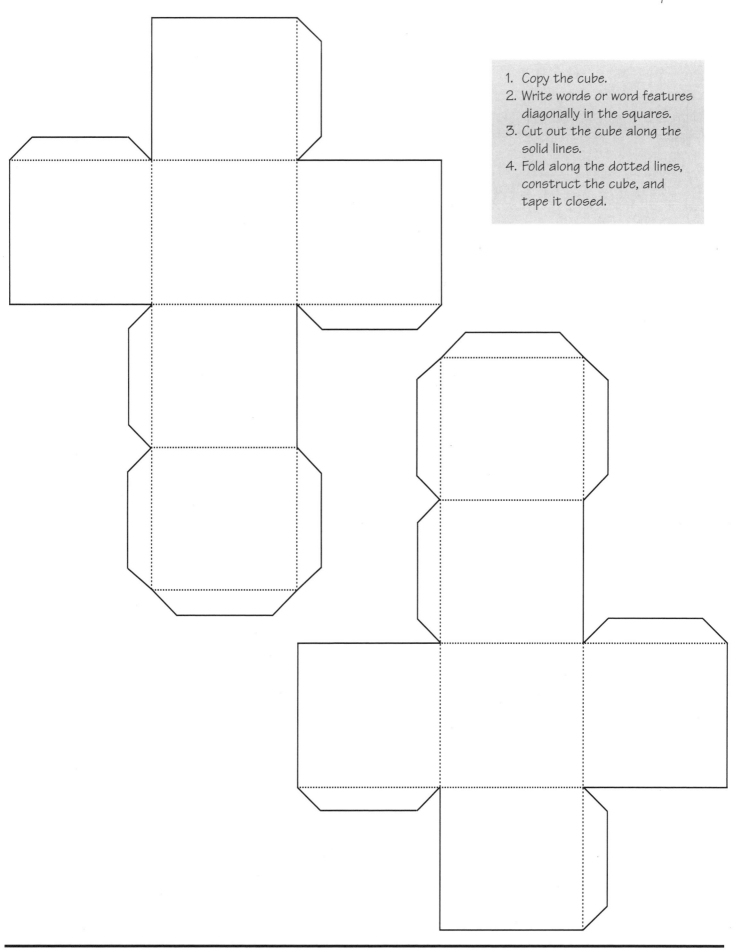

1. Copy the cube.
2. Write words or word features diagonally in the squares.
3. Cut out the cube along the solid lines.
4. Fold along the dotted lines, construct the cube, and tape it closed.

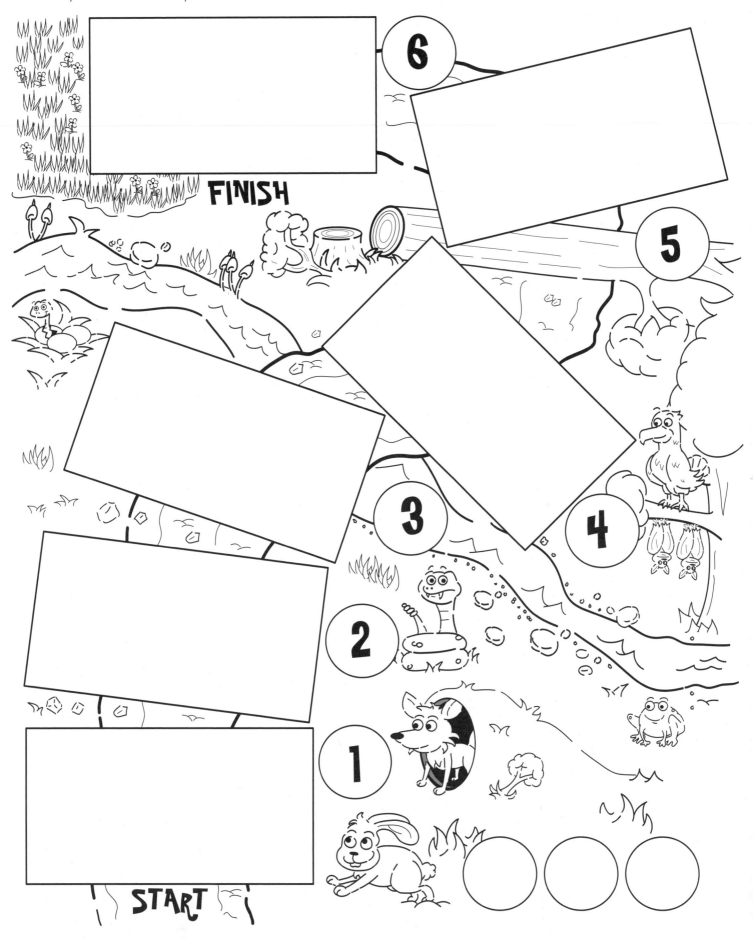

FINISH

6

5

3

4

2

1

START